WELCOME TO JAMAA

GRAHAM'S WORKSHOP

Written by ERIC M. ESQUIVEL
Art by TONY FLEECS
Color by MOHAN
Letters by TOM NAPOLITANO

Issue Covers By
FERNANDO RUIZ & PETE PANTAZIS
TONY FLEECS

Edited by
ANTHONY MARQUES

Collection cover by
FERNANDO RUIZ & PETE PANTAZIS

Collection design by
CATHLEEN HEARD

DYNAMITE®

Barrucci, CEO / Publisher
Collado, President / COO

Rybandt, Executive Editor
Idelson, Senior Editor
hony Marques, Associate Editor
Ketner, Assistant Editor

on Ullmeyer, Art Director
ff Harkins, Senior Graphic Designer
leen Heard, Graphic Designer
xis Persson, Graphic Designer

s Caniano, Digital Associate
el Kilbury, Digital Assistant

ndon Dante Primavera, V.P. of IT and Operations
Young, Director of Business Development

Payne, V.P. of Sales and Marketing
e MacKenzie, Marketing Coordinator
O'Connell, Sales Manager

Online at www.DYNAMITE.com
On Facebook /Dynamitecomics
On Instagram /Dynamitecomics
On Tumblr dynamitecomics.tumblr.com
On Twitter @dynamitecomics
On YouTube /Dynamitecomics

WILDWORKS

Hardcover Edition:
ISBN-13: 978-1-5241-0386-6
Scholastic Paperback:
ISBN-13: 978-1-5241-0387-3
First Printing
10 9 8 7 6 5 4 3 2 1

PEFC Certified
Printed on paper from
sustainably managed
forests and controlled
sources
PEFC
PEFC/01-31-106   www.pefc.org

Issue #0: Cover Art by **FERNANDO RUIZ** & **PETE PANTAZIS**

THIS PLACE IS AMAZING!

IT SURE IS!

MY NAME IS PECK AND I'M HERE TO SHOW YOU AROUND JAMAA!

WHAT IS JAMAA?

JAMAA IS A WONDERFUL PLACE WHERE THOUSANDS OF ANIMALS OF ALL DIFFERENT SPECIES HAVE COME TO LIVE AND PLAY IN PEACE.

WE HAVE FUN AND WORK TOGETHER AS FRIENDS!

THERE IS SO MUCH TO SHOW YOU AND SO MANY NEW FRIENDS TO INTRODUCE YOU TO...I CAN'T WAIT!

C'MON! LET'S GO!

ULP!

PECK ALWAYS SEEMS TO BE IN A HURRY.

GASP!

MY NAME IS SIR GILBERT.

WELCOME TO JAMAA, YOUNG ONE!

TH... THANK YOU, SIR!

MY NAME IS CLOVER!

HI, CLOVER!

MY NAME IS LIZA, AND I LOVE TO MEET ALL THE NEW ANIMALS THAT COME TO JAMAA.

KE SIR LBERT D PECK, M ONE F THE PHAS.

AN ALPHA?! WHAT'S AN ALPHA?

THE ALPHAS ARE THE LEADERS OF JAMAA. WE WORK HARD TO PROTECT JAMAA AND ALL THE ANIMALS THAT WANT TO LIVE HERE IN PEACE AND FRIENDSHIP FROM THE TERRIBLE PHANTOMS.

PHANTOMS? WHAT ARE THE PHANTOMS?

THEY ARE ROTTEN CREATURES WHO WANT NOTHING MORE THAN TO DESTROY JAMAA AND RUIN ALL OF OUR FUN.

MANY YEARS AGO, THE ANIMALS OF JAMAA LIVED APART AND DIDN'T WORK TOGETHER TO STOP THE PHANTOMS WHEN THEY FIRST ARRIVED.

THE PHANTOMS QUICKLY MOVED ACROSS JAMAA DESTROYING EVERYTHING.

"ZIOS AND MIRA, THE GUARDIAN SPIRITS OF JAMAA, BROUGHT TOGETHER THE SIX ALPHAS TO UNITE ALL OF THE ANIMAL SPECIES AND DRIVE AWAY THE PHANTOMS."

GULP! WHAT IF THESE PHANTOMS COME BACK?

THE ALPHAS KEEP VIGILANT WATCH OVER JAMAA, READY TO DRIVE BACK THE PHANTOMS IF THEY EVER APPEAR.

HEY! WHERE DID YOU GO? I THOUGHT YOU WERE RIGHT BEHIND ME?

NOBODY CAN KEEP UP WITH PECK!

YEESH! I CAN SEE THAT!

LET'S GO! WE'VE GOT LOTS MORE TO SHOW YOU!

YES INDEED! JAMAA IS A BIG WONDERFUL PLACE!

AND WE'VE GOT TO INTRODUCE YOU TO THE OTHER ALPHAS!

OH BOY! I CAN'T WAIT! THIS IS EXCITING!

AND SO...

Graham's Workshop! Keep Out!

THIS IS GRAHAM'S WORKSHOP. GRAHAM IS AN ALPHA LIKE US.

UH... THE SIGN SAYS "KEEP OUT."

HA! GRAHAM GETS SO CAUGHT UP IN HIS WORK THAT HE PROBABLY WON'T EVEN NOTICE WE'RE HERE!

WOW! WHAT IS ALL THIS?

GRAHAM IS A...AH...A BIT OF A TINKERER.

A TINKERER?! HE BUILT THAT? WHAT DOES IT DO?

I AM NOT SURE. GRAHAM OFTEN FORGETS TO TELL US WHAT HE IS WORKING ON.

LOOK--!

EEK!

OH, DON'T LET COSMO'S CHOMPER PLANTS SCARE YOU, CLOVER...

THE CHOMPER PLANTS ONLY EVER SNAP SHUT AROUND PHANTOMS!

YEAH. THEY'VE BEEN VERY USEFUL IN TRAPPING PHANTOMS!

EWWW!

THAT COSMO HAS QUITE THE GREEN THUMB...ER... PAW!

HA! THAT'S NOTHING! WE'VE GOT LOTS MORE EXCITING THINGS TO SHOW YOU!

YEAH! C'MON!

AND SO...

SEE? I TOLD YOU WE HAD MORE INTERESTING STUFF TO SHOW YOU!

WHAT IS *THAT*?

THAT, MY DEAR IS...

THE LOST TEMPLE OF ZIOS!

WHA... WHAT IS THIS PLACE?

LONG AGO, THIS IS WHERE THE ANIMALS OF JAMAA KEPT THEIR HEARTSTONES... SPECIAL STONES THAT CONTAINED THE ESSENCE AND POWER OF THEIR ENTIRE SPECIES.

WHEN THE ANIMALS OF JAMAA BEGAN TO DISTRUST ONE ANOTHER...

...THEY SEPARATED THEMSELVES INTO ISOLATED VILLAGES, AND TOOK THEIR HEARTSTONES WITH THEM.

WHEN THEY DID SO, THAT ANIMAL SPECIES DISAPPEARED FROM JAMAA.

WHEN THE PHANTOMS CAME, THEY WERE EASILY ABLE TO PICK OFF THE SMALL VILLAGES AND CAPTURE THE HEARTSTONES.

NOW ALL OF US ARE ALWAYS ON A QUEST TO FIND THE LOST HEARSTONES AND RETURN THEM HERE.

THE HEARTSTONES MAKE IT POSSIBLE FOR ANIMALS TO LIVE IN JAMAA. WHENEVER A LOST HEARTSTONE IS DISCOVERED AND RETURNED TO JAMAA, THAT ANIMAL SPECIES CAN NOW LIVE HERE.

WE'VE BEEN STANDING STILL TOO LONG!

LET'S SHOW CLOVER *MORE!*

Issue #1: Cover Art by **FERNANDO RUIZ** & **PETE PANTAZIS**

THE TROJAN ELEPHANT

STORY & ART BY FERNANDO RUIZ
COLOR BY PETE PANTAZIS
LETTERING BY TOM NAPOLITANO
EDITING BY ANTHONY MARQUES

HEY COSMO, WANNA RACE?

HA! YOU GOT IT, PECK, BUT YOU BETTER HUSTLE...

...FROM UP HERE, I CAN EASILY SWING TO VICTORY!

KNOCK IT OFF, YOU TWO.

EEP!

OH, COME ON, GREELY. LEARN TO HAVE A LITTLE FUN!

WE ARE HERE TO LOOK FOR PHANTOM ACTIVITY, NOT TO HAVE FUN.

NOBODY HAS EVER BEEN THIS DEEP INTO SAREPIA FOREST BEFORE. WE NEED TO BE CAUTIOUS.

BUT CAN'T WE BE CAREFUL AND HAVE FUN?

AT THE RATE WE WERE GOING, COSMO AND I WERE GOING TO COVER MORE GROUND FASTER!

LOOK OUT!

EEK!

WHAT ARE THOSE?

THEY'RE VINES! BUT THEY SURE GREW IN AN INCONVENIENT SPOT!

THIS DIDN'T HAPPEN NATURALLY. THIS IS A TRAP.

A TRAP?!

YES. LOOK OVER THERE.

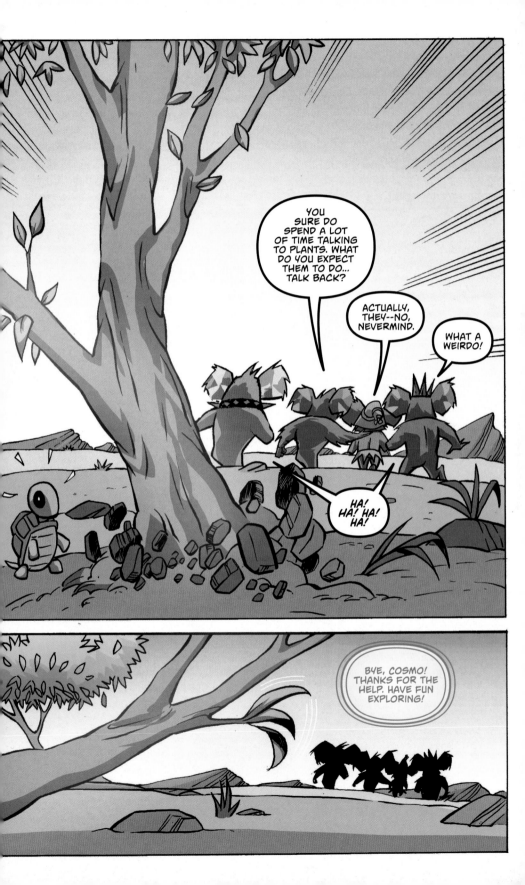

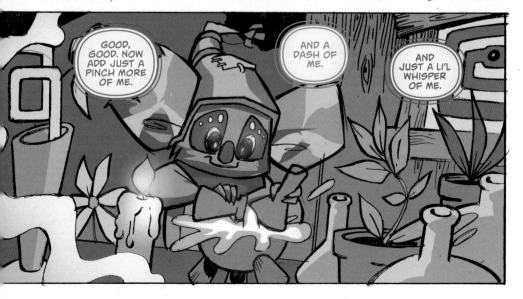

SO, YOU CAME HERE TO GLOAT?

NOPE. I CAME HERE TO HELP.

WHY WOULD YOU HELP US? WE BULLIED THE LIVING DAYLIGHTS OUTTA YOU.

HOW YOU CHOOSE TO BEHAVE IS NONE OF MY BUSINESS. I CAN ONLY CONTROL MY OWN ACTIONS, AND *I* CHOOSE TO *HEAL* RATHER THAN *HURT*.

HERE, TRY THIS. IT'S MY OWN SPECIAL RECIPE.

MAN, THAT REALLY HITS THE SPOT!

THE ITCHINESS IS GONE!

NO MORE FIRE ANTS ON MY BOTTOM!

ZIOS, DO YOU SEE THIS?

I DO, MIRA. WHAT A KIND AND NOBLE SOUL. HE WOULD MAKE AN *EXCELLENT* ALPHA.

AGREED.

WHAT CAN I DO TO REPAY YOU?

MAYBE BE NICE TO EVERYONE FROM NOW ON? NO MORE BULLYING?

YOU GOT IT, COSMO!

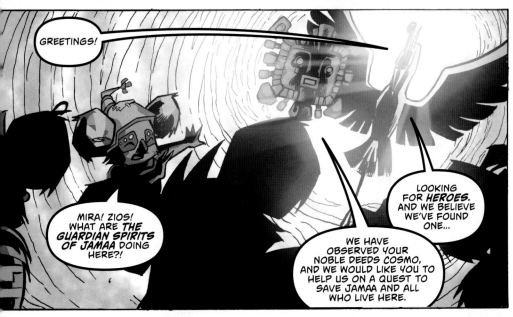

GREETINGS!

MIRA! ZIOS! WHAT ARE *THE GUARDIAN SPIRITS OF JAMAA* DOING HERE?!

LOOKING FOR *HEROES*. AND WE BELIEVE WE'VE FOUND ONE...

WE HAVE OBSERVED YOUR NOBLE DEEDS COSMO, AND WE WOULD LIKE YOU TO HELP US ON A QUEST TO SAVE JAMAA AND ALL WHO LIVE HERE.

ME? ARE YOU SURE?

GO GET 'EM, COSMO!

YOU TOTALLY GOT THIS!

DO IT!

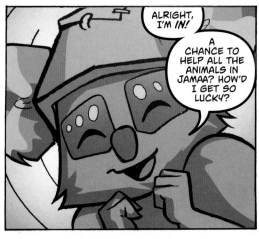

ALRIGHT, I'M *IN!*

A CHANCE TO HELP ALL THE ANIMALS IN JAMAA? HOW'D I GET SO LUCKY?

Issue #2: Cover Art by **FERNANDO RUIZ & PETE PANTAZIS**

IT LOOKS LIKE THE ENTRANCE TO AN OLD MINE SHAFT!

IT LOOKS PRETTY OLD. I WONDER WHO BUILT IT!

I HAVE NO IDEA. IT LOOKS LIKE IT'S BEEN HERE FOR AGES, SINCE WAY BEFORE WE WERE CALLED AS ALPHAS.

C'MON! LET'S CHECK IT OUT!

UH...!

I DON'T KNOW, PECK. THAT SHAFT LOOKS DEEP...AND DARK!

OH, C'MON, COSMO!

DON'T YOU WANT TO SEE WHERE IT GOES?

GULP! I DON'T LIKE PLACES WHERE I CAN'T CLIMB...

...OR THAT ARE TOO DARK!

WAIT! THERE'S A LIGHT UP AHEAD!

COSMO! LOOK! IT'S A JEWEL OF SOME KIND...AND IT GLOWS!

IT'S BEAUTIFUL. I WONDER...

UH, PECK...? WHAT'S *THAT*?

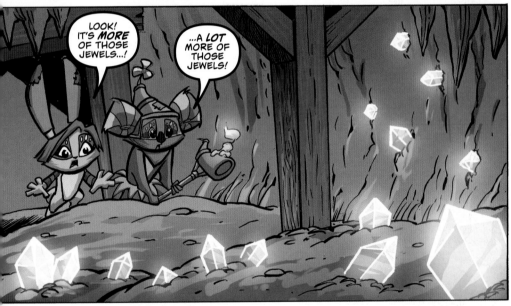

LOOK! IT'S *MORE* OF THOSE JEWELS...!

...A *LOT* MORE OF THOSE JEWELS!

JUST IMAGINE ALL THE FUN WE COULD HAVE WITH THESE IF WE TOOK THEM BACK TO JAMAA TOWNSHIP!

EVERYONE WOULD LOOK SO COOL WEARING THEM!

WE CAN USE THIS TUFF TO MINE A BUNCH OF THESE JEWELS OURSELVES!

WAIT UNTIL EVERYONE SEES HOW BEAUTIFUL THESE ARE!

EVERYONE'S GONNA LOVE THESE!

YEAH! LET'S GET STARTED SO WE CAN BRING A WHOLE BUNCH BACK WITH US!

WOW! LOOK AT THIS PLACE!

CAN YOU IMAGINE WHAT THIS PLACE LOOKED LIKE WHEN THE MINE WAS OPERATIONAL?

OKAY! LET'S GET STARTED...!

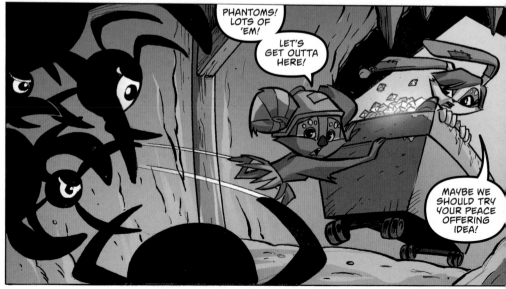

...YOU'VE ALSO GOT FRIENDS!

LET'S GO, EVERYBODY!

GET THEM!

WATCH OUT FOR THE PHANTOMS!

WAH-HOO!

GO GET 'EM!

THE PHANTOMS ARE ON THE RUN...

THEY NO DOUBT WILL MAKE A STRATEGIC WITHDRAWAL!

SIR GILBERT! BUT HOW DID YOU KNOW WE WERE IN TROUBLE?

SOME OF OUR FRIENDS TOLD US WHAT YOU TWO WERE UP TO.

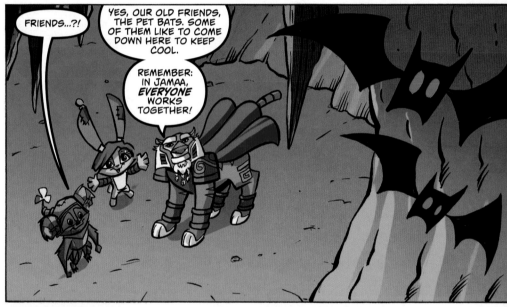

FRIENDS...?!

YES, OUR OLD FRIENDS, THE PET BATS. SOME OF THEM LIKE TO COME DOWN HERE TO KEEP COOL.

REMEMBER: IN JAMAA, *EVERYONE* WORKS TOGETHER!

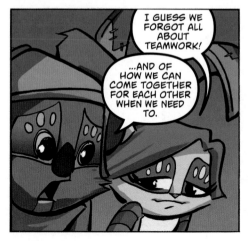

I GUESS WE FORGOT ALL ABOUT TEAMWORK!

...AND OF HOW WE CAN COME TOGETHER FOR EACH OTHER WHEN WE NEED TO.

NOW REALIZING *THAT* IS A *REAL* TREASURE!

YEAH! AND WE CAN GET THAT ONE WITH A WHOLE LOT LESS DIGGING!

END

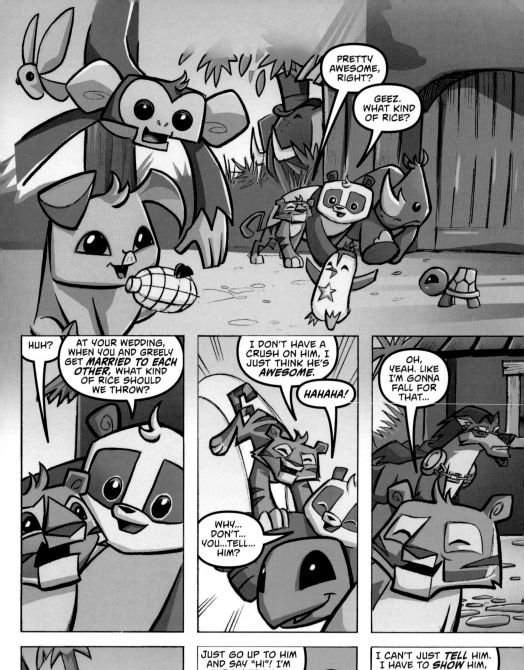

MONTHS OF PLANNING, HUNTING, SNEAKING AROUND **FINALLY** PAY OFF. I KNEW THE PHANTOMS WERE UP TO SOMETHING **ROTTEN**, BUT I NEVER GUESSED IT WAS SOMETHING **THIS BIG.**

I HAVE TO MAKE MY NEXT MOVE **CAREFULLY.** ONE FALSE STEP AND--

CRUNCH

?

WHO ARE **YOU?** WHAT ARE YOU **DOING** HERE?

WHOOPSIE.

SNAPPED TWIG

I'M, UH, YOUR...YOUR NUMBER ONE FAN?

GROWL

YOU HAVE AN INTERESTING WAY OF SHOWING IT.

GULP

I'M SORRY! I WAS JUST TRYING TO HELP!

IF YOU WANT TO HELP...

...GET AS FAR AWAY FROM HERE AS POSSIBLE.

GROWL

MY PLAN WAS WORKING PERFECTLY UNTIL YOU ARRIVED.

GO! BEFORE YOU RUIN ANYTHING ELSE!

THAT'S RIGHT, *SCRAM!*

I'M REAL SORRY FOR MESSING THINGS UP EARLIER, GREELY. IF IT WASN'T FOR ME, YOU--

--COULD HAVE GOTTEN SERIOUSLY HURT. OR POSSIBLY *WORSE.* THANK YOU, YOUNG ONE.

WITH THE BRAVERY YOU SHOWED TODAY, IT SEEMS THAT I AM *YOUR* NUMBER ONE FAN.

END

Issue #3: Cover Art by **FERNANDO RUIZ** & **PETE PANTAZIS**

WELL *THAT* WAS DISAPPOINTING...

THEY RUN FROM FAKE PHANTOMS? WHAT ARE THEY GOING TO DO WHEN THEY FACE THE REAL THINGS?

DID YOU REALLY HAVE TO RUIN OUR WALK, GREELY?

THE PHANTOMS CAN ATTACK ANYWHERE AT ANYTIME.

IT'S IMPORTANT THAT WE NEVER FORGET THAT!

BUT IF WE CAN'T TAKE A BREAK FROM FOCUSING ON THE PHANTOMS TO ACTUALLY ENJOY JAMAA, WHAT ARE WE FIGHTING FOR?

IF THE PHANTOMS EVER GET THEIR WAY, THERE WON'T BE ANY OF JAMAA LEFT TO ENJOY.

LATER BACK AT JAMAA TOWNSHIP...

LET YOUR GUARD DOWN IF YOU WISH, BUT I CERTAINLY AM NOT GOING TO LET THE PHANTOMS GET THE JUMP ON ME.

THOSE TWO NEED SOMETHING NEW TO OCCUPY THEM.

SIR GILBERT! GREELY! I'M GLAD YOU'RE HERE!

I'VE BEEN HEARING RUMORS THAT A LARGE SNOW BEAST HAS BEEN SEEN UP ON MT. SHIVEER!

AS ALPHAS, I THINK WE SHOULD CHECK IT OUT!

A SNOW BEAST? HOW CURIOUS.

THIS COULD BE THE WORK OF THE PHANTOMS. LET'S GO!

THAT'S THE SPIRIT!

...TOGETHERRR!!!

OH NO! LIZA, WATCH OUT FOR THE ICE!

TOO LATE. SHE'S OUT OF CONTROL!

PLOP

OOF!

WHOOOAAA!!

GROAN! I MUST'VE SLID HALF WAY DOWN MT. SHIVEER!

I BETTER FIND MY WAY BACK TO THE OTHERS...

UH-OH!

IT'S THE SNOW BEAST!

HEY! WAIT A MINUTE!

THERE'S SOMETHING AWFULLY STRANGE ABOUT THIS SNOW BEAST.

IT'S NOT REAL! IT'S A BIG GIANT DUMMY!

WHAT COULD GRAHAM HAVE IN THERE THAT THE PHANTOMS WANT?

Graham's Workshop
COME ON IN!
Unless you're a *Phantom*

MAYBE HE INVENTED SOMETHING THAT COULD HELP OUR FIGHT AGAINST THE PHANTOMS AND THEY WANT TO GET RID OF IT?

THERE IS ONLY ONE WAY TO FIND OUT.

NO, NO. I KNOW *EXACTLY* WHAT THIS IS...

OH?

OF COURSE. IT'S REALLY QUITE SIMPLE, ONCE YOU SEE IT...

HAPPY DAY! Festi

IT'S SOME SORT OF REVERED MONKEY HOLIDAY DECORATION.

MMMAYBE.

BUT IS IT *LIKELY?*

I DON'T BLAME YOU GUYS FOR NOT SEEING IT, BUT MY *HIGHLY TUNED* SENSES TELL ME THAT THIS THING IS...

YOINK

...AN *AWESOME,* PHANTOM-BONKING *WEAPON!*

SERIOUSLY?

BONUS COVERS

Issue #1: Gameplay Cover Art

Issue #2: Cover Art by TONY FLEECS

Issue #3: Cover Art by **TONY FLEECS**

THE
ALPHAS

Sir Gilbert

TRAITS:

Skills-	Strength, strategy, leadership
Personality-	Regal, friendly, commanding, genuine
Likes-	Justice, storytelling
Dislikes-	Evil
Weakness-	Stubborn
Goal-	Stop the Phantoms once and for all
Inner Voice-	"Everyone is counting on me. I cannot fail."

Liza

TRAITS:

Skills- Intuition, diplomacy, adventurous spirit

Personality- Reserved, focused, warm

Likes- Exploring, reading, photography

Dislikes- Inequality

Weakness- Overly-compassionate

Goal- Unite the animals of Jamaa

Inner Voice- "I hope I can be there for everyone."

Greely

TRAITS:

Skills-	Stealth, observation, knowledge
Personality-	Mysterious, quiet, terse
Likes-	Solitude
Dislikes-	Parties
Weakness-	Doesn't trust others
Goal-	Learn everything possible about the dark Phantoms
Inner Voice-	"The only one who will never let me down is me."

Peck

TRAITS:

Skills-	Creativity, art, music
Personality-	Talented, energetic, happy
Likes-	All kinds of art
Dislikes-	Sitting still
Weakness-	Impulsive
Goal-	Make Jamaa as cheerful and peaceful as possible
Inner Voice-	"The world of Jamaa is such a beautiful and fascinating place!"

COSMO

TRAITS:

Skills- Knowledge, resourcefulness, ability to speak with plants

Personality- Clever, youthful, introverted

Likes- Plants, jokes

Dislikes- Confrontation

Weakness- Timid

Goal- Help keep Jamaa clean and beautiful

Inner Voice- "One day, I hope everyone will be able to get along."

GRAHAM

TRAITS:

Skills-	Ingenuity, creativity, innovation
Personality-	Intelligent, focused, jovial
Likes-	Inventing, tinkering, puzzles
Dislikes-	When things don't work
Weakness-	A bit scatterbrained
Goal-	Learn the "what", "how", and "why" of everything
Inner Voice-	"The world is filled with fascination."